BRYOPHYTES OF N

A Field Guide to
Common Mosses and Liverworts of
Britain and Ireland's Woodlands

Third edition

Carol L Crawford

Published by The Natural Resource Consultancy for the
Native Woodlands Discussion Group
LOWER PLANTS SECTION

NATURAL RESOURCE CONSULTANCY

EAMONN WALL & CO.
WOODLAND DESIGN AND MANAGEMENT

treefest
scotland2002

NATIVE
WOODLANDS
DISCUSSION
GROUP

Preparation

Acknowledgements

I am grateful to everyone who provided help and advice during the preparation of this guide, in particular to Ben Averis for: bryophyte ID, correcting the proof, advice on common names, three photos, etc. Thanks also to:

Alison Averis; Flexible Learning Centre, Ayr College; Stella Crawford; Helen Gray; Gordon Gray Stephens, John Parrott and colleagues at Scottish Native Woods; Lesley Findlay at Clydeprint Ltd; Phil James; Jessops of Ayr; Ernest Law and colleagues at MFST; Native Woodlands Discussion Group committee members; Karl Partridge; Ken Paterson; Peter Quelch; Frank and Florence Sloan, Drumcovitt Lodge, Feeny, NI; Eamonn Wall; and Tom Walsh, The Laptop Centre, Glasgow.

Publication details

Published by The Natural Resource Consultancy (TNRC)
First published March 2001
Second Edition February 2002
(1st and 2nd editions sub-titled: A.....Scotland and Ireland's Native Woodlands)
This edition November 2002
Printers (of all editions): Clydeprint Ltd
ISBN 0 — 9543795 — 0— 0

The guide was produced with a Millennium Award, through the Millennium Forest for Scotland Trust. The second edition was sponsored by Scottish Natural Heritage and Eamonn Wall and Co. This third edition was funded by: donations from recipients of the second edition, the Native Woodlands Discussion Group, Treefest, TNRC and Eamonn Wall and Co.

The third edition is the first to be offered for sale. All profits will go towards a second volume of common woodland bryophytes, for the British Isles as a whole.

Further copies available from the author (address inside back cover) for £6.50 including p&p within Britain (£7/€11 overseas). Cheques payable to TNRC.

Photographic details

The author's photographs were taken with a Nikon Coolpix 950 digital camera, in Scotland and Ireland, between October 2000 and September 2001. Ben Averis used a Nikon Coolpix 990 for his shots (in East Lothian).

"Group" shots were taken at: Artilligan and Barnluasgan Forests and the banks of Loch Lomond, Argyll; Burnhouse Brae, Craigencroy Glen, Culzean Country Park and Woodroad Park, Ayrshire; Whittingehame, Garvald, Dirleton and Whiteadder Water, East Lothian; the Birks of Aberfeldy and the Black Wood of Rannoch, Tayside; Killarney National Park particularly Derrycunihy and Reenadinna Woods, Eire; Breen Oakwood Nature Reserve, Ballycastle, and Banagher Glen Nature Reserve and Ness Wood Country Park, Derry, Northern Ireland.

*The liverwort on front cover is **Pellia epiphylla***

The mossy oak on inside title page was taken in Banagher Glen.

Contents

Glossary — Inside front cover

Introduction — 4

Sphagnum mosses — Bog Mosses — 6
Sphagnum capillifolium/quinquefarium — 6
Sphagnum fallax — 7
Sphagnum palustre — 8

Acrocarpous mosses — 9
Leucobryum glaucum — White Moss — 9
Polytrichum commune — Marsh Hair Moss — 10
Polytrichum formosum — Wood Hair Moss — 11
Dicranum scoparium — Fork Moss — 12
Dicranum majus — Great Fork Moss — 13
Atrichum undulatum — Catherine's Moss — 14
Plagiomnium undulatum — Palm Moss — 15
Mnium hornum — Forest Star — 16
Rhizomnium punctatum — Round Moss — 17

Pleurocarpous mosses — 18
Thuidium tamariscinum — Tamarisk Moss — 18
Hylocomium splendens — Step Moss — 19
Isothecium myosuroides — Mouse-tail — 20
Isothecium alopecuroides — Big Mouse-tail — 21
Eurhynchium striatum — Stripe Moss — 22
Eurhynchium praelongum — Feather Moss — 23
Calliergonella cuspidata — Spear Moss — 24
Brachythecium rutabulum — Ordinary Moss — 25
Scleropodium purum — Neat Moss — 26
Pleurozium schreberi — Red-stem — 27
Plagiothecium undulatum — Wavy Flat Moss — 28
Ptilium crista-castrensis — Plume Moss — 29
Hypnum cupressiforme complex — Cypress Mosses — 30
Rhytidiadelphus squarrosus — Lawn Moss — 32
Rhytidiadelphus loreus — Stiff Moss — 33
Rhytidiadelphus triquetrus — Shaggy Moss — 34

Liverworts — 35
Diplophyllum albicans — Doublewort — 35
Lophocolea bidentata — Pincerwort — 36
Pellia epiphylla — Dripwort — 37

Commonest bryophytes in NVC wood types — 38

References and sources of information — 40

Introduction

The aim of this booklet is to help people identify common mosses and liverworts, plants which are often overlooked because of their small size and long Latin names. It is also hoped that the booklet will increase appreciation of these plants and encourage people to study them more.

Why study mosses and liverworts?

Studying bryophytes is very rewarding. They are beautiful and can be found all year round. Indeed, in winter, when much else is dull and bare, they add colour to the forest floor and sometimes to trees themselves.

For ecologists and forest managers they can provide valuable clues to site conditions such as geology and soil type. Vegetation surveyors using the National Vegetation Classification (NVC), now the standard British system, often require knowledge of bryophytes to identify different woodland types. Ecological data in NVC volumes can then be accessed.

Selection of bryophytes for booklet

This booklet contains information on 33 common mosses and three common liverworts of native woodlands. They were selected as the commonest bryophytes in Scottish woods (the author analysed data in the NVC woodland volume (Rodwell,1991) and Ben Averis added several species, from his extensive sampling since that volume was compiled). Nearly all these species are commonly encountered in woods throughout north and west Britain.

In fact all but two species (*Sphagnum quinquefarium* and *Ptilium crista-castrensis)* are widespread in Britain and Ireland.

Equipment for studying bryophytes

Little equipment is required: a x 10 hand lens; plastic bags to collect specimens; A4 paper to fold into envelopes for specimens when dry; a pen to record names and where and when found; a shoe box to hold the herbarium envelopes. One advantage of studying bryophytes is that dried specimens can be restored with water then used for further study.

This booklet covers features which can be seen with a naked eye or a hand lens; usually enough to identify common bryophytes. If there is still confusion between similar species, additional features can be viewed under a microscope. These features are covered in Smith's (1978 and 1990) floras, which also include close-up drawings. Other useful books are given on Page 40 of this booklet, under References. More information on bryophyte biology can also be found in these books.

Arrangement of this booklet

Mosses are arranged in their three groups: *Sphagnum*, Pleurocarps and Acrocarps (for definitions see glossary). Within each group they are loosely ordered as per Blockeel and Long (1998), but species between which there is most confusion are placed on facing pages. Two Leafy Liverworts are given next and a Thalloid Liverwort last.

On most pages there is a large photograph showing a collection of stems at the top, and smaller photographs of single stems or leaf arrangements at the sides or bottom. All pictures on a page are of the moss named in the header, except on the *Sphagnum capillifolium/ quinquefarium* and *Hypnum cupressiforme* pages where more than one species is covered.

Bryophytes do not have strictly-defined common names. Informal English names are given in the page headers. These were chosen from British Bryological Society combined lists or amended to give short, simple aide-memoires. **Note** Latin names should still be used in survey reports.

The text on each page is arranged in coloured boxes as per the key below. It includes a list of the main woodland NVC types in Scotland within which each species is found. However most species will be found in other woodland types that contain its microhabitat(s). Microhabitats are also given for each species.

The table on Pages 38 and 39 lists the commonest bryophytes found in each Scottish woodland NVC community and, where there are differences, in individual sub-communities. This table also serves as a key to the NVC codes on each bryophyte page.

Key to the text

The **pale green** boxes describe the large-scale **Habitats**, including non-woodland types, in which each bryophyte is found.

The **dark green** boxes give the NVC codes for the woodland communities in which a species is commonly present in Scotland (from W1 - W19).

The **pale blue** boxes list local places within woods where each species occurs. **Note** a species can be found in such places in other than the main NVC types.

The **dark blue** boxes highlight physical conditions such as soil types, moisture and light requirements. The blue boxes together describe **Microhabitats.**

The **beige** boxes describe **Key Identification Features** which can be seen with a hand lens, e.g. stem colour and branching, leaf shape and colour.

The **pale pink** boxes cover species which may be confused with the bryophyte on that page. The main distinguishing features are described.

Where closely related species are covered on one page they are named in **dark pink** boxes. **Note** photos beside pink boxes are of the species in page header.

Sphagnum capillifolium/quinquefarium

S. capillifolium - photos above

Habitats
Bogs, moors, heaths and woods.

Main NVC woodland types:
W18d, W18e.

Microhabitats
Drier parts of acid peatlands above water table, carpets under heather.

Key ID features
Nearly always red-tinted but can be green tinged with pink or green in shade. Delicate moss which forms compact cushions or carpets.

Both these *Sphagnum* spp. are small-medium sized mosses with well developed capitula and prominent appressed, erect stem leaves. *S. quinquefarium* often has more branches per fascicle (4 - 5) than *S. capillifolium* (3 - 4). Both spp. have distinct pendent and spreading branches.

S. quinquefarium - photos below

Habitats
Damp hillsides, birch and pine woods.

Main NVC woodland types:
W17, W18d/e.

Microhabitats
Moist sheltered banks. Not on waterlogged ground, rarely on peat.

Key ID features
Usually green or pale yellow-green but can be red-flecked.

Tall stiff moss with close-set leaves, giving branches an angular appearance, and dense shoot tips.

Sphagnum fallax

Habitats
Birch and willow woodlands, various types of mire.

Main NVC woodland types:
W4b, W4c.

Key ID features
Pale stems to 20 cm with lax, well-spaced branches. 4 - 6 branches per fascicle, 2 - 3 spreading, 2 - 4 pendent. Latter appressed to stem and whitish. Tufted head to stem.

Stem leaves are tiny, wide-spaced and hang downwards. Branch leaves are recurved when dry, the tips appearing hooked.

Microhabitats
Pools, ditches and their margins, flushes, *Sphagnum* lawns, woodland floor.

Acid wet ground. Can be submerged.

Could be confused with:
Sphagnum cuspidatum is a more aquatic peatland plant. Its pendent branches are less well-defined from spreading branches and it has much longer branch leaves than *S. fallax*.

Sphagnum fimbriatum. In this species the stem leaves point upwards and have broad, blunt, tattered tips. It has a large conical bud at top of stem.

Ben Averis

7

Sphagnum palustre

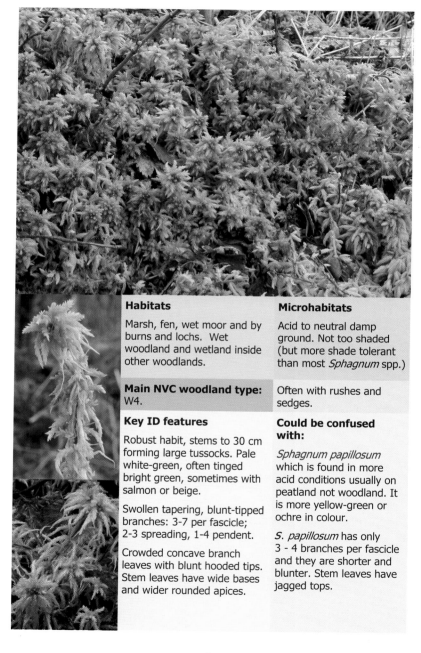

Habitats

Marsh, fen, wet moor and by burns and lochs. Wet woodland and wetland inside other woodlands.

Main NVC woodland type: W4.

Key ID features

Robust habit, stems to 30 cm forming large tussocks. Pale white-green, often tinged bright green, sometimes with salmon or beige.

Swollen tapering, blunt-tipped branches: 3-7 per fascicle; 2-3 spreading, 1-4 pendent.

Crowded concave branch leaves with blunt hooded tips. Stem leaves have wide bases and wider rounded apices.

Microhabitats

Acid to neutral damp ground. Not too shaded (but more shade tolerant than most *Sphagnum* spp.)

Often with rushes and sedges.

Could be confused with:

Sphagnum papillosum which is found in more acid conditions usually on peatland not woodland. It is more yellow-green or ochre in colour.

S. papillosum has only 3 - 4 branches per fascicle and they are shorter and blunter. Stem leaves have jagged tops.

Leucobryum glaucum White Moss

Habitats

Heath, blanket bog and other moorland, broadleaved and conifer woodlands.

Main NVC woodland types:
W15, W16, W17.

Key ID features

A fairly unique moss. Densely tufted, forming cushions which can extend to 1 m across and can rise to 15 cm. White-green to glaucous leaves. Shoots dirty white or grey and semi-decayed with short green tips.

Leaves crowded on stem, lanceolate, to 10 mm long, narrowing to a blunt point. Broad nerve occupies most of leaf base.

Plant is porous, holding water like a sponge as in *Sphagnum* species.

Microhabitats

Acid to strongly acid substrate: leached soil, humus, peat, leaf mould and acid rocks.

Forest floor, rocks, tree stumps. On trees in wet areas.

Could be confused with:

Small compact *Dicranum* species. These have yellow to dark green leaves and brown stems. They do not form massive cushions or absorb water like *L. glaucum.*

Polytrichum commune Marsh Hair Moss

Habitats	**Microhabitats**
Usually a plant of wet heath, bog and damp moor. Also in wet woodland particularly:	Often with *Sphagnum* species. By woodland watercourses.
Main NVC woodland type: W4.	Damp acid soil, including peat.

Key ID features

Generally 15 – 20 cm tall. Can reach 40 cm.

Leaves 8 – 12 mm, narrow all along with pale glossy sheathing bases. Leaves can be glaucous.

Capsule on tall reddish seta (6 – 12 cm). Capsule 4-sided, length little greater than width, can appear cubic when ripe. Beak 1 mm.

Could be confused with:

Polytrichum formosum.

Both *Polytrichum* spp. have rigid stems and long leaves which narrow to a fine toothed point. Leaves stick out when moist and close into stem when dry.

P. commune is taller and its leaves more widely spaced. Its leaves stick straight out when moist.

P. formosum capsule is rarely 4-sided and is longer, with a longer beak.

Polytrichum formosum Wood Hair Moss

Habitats

Upland heaths, grasslands and oak/birch woods particularly:

Main NVC woodland types:

W11, W16, W17, W19.

Key ID features

Generally 5 – 10 cm tall. Can reach 20 cm.

Leaves dull green and often orange-edged. They are wide at base, narrowing to tip.

Seta 2.5 – 6 cm, yellow above, red below. Capsule usually 5 – 6 angled with 2 mm beak.

Microhabitats

Prefers well-drained acid soils. Also on strongly acid or neutral soil.

Often on banks.

Could be confused with:

Polytrichum commune.

Polytrichum formosum is shorter and its leaves closer together. Leaves are more curved when moist and do not have light glossy sheaths.

Polytrichum commune seta is red all the way up.

Dicranum scoparium   Fork Moss

Habitats
Moorland, heath, bog, grassland etc. Often in woods particularly:

Microhabitats
Banks, tree bases, bark, branches, rotting wood, rocks, walls.

Main NVC woodland types: W11, W16, W17, W18, W19.

Wide range of conditions. From strong acid to neutral soils including humus.

Key ID features
Generally 2 -10 cm tall forming dense tufts. Robust erect habit. Variable species.

Leaves lanceolate, 4 - 8 mm long, slightly curved to one side or straight. Typically bright yellow-green; can be mid-green. Orange-brown patches at bases of leaves. Leaf tip variably toothed.

Reddish-yellow seta 3 - 4 cm long bears single, curved cylindrical capsule with long, obliquely beaked lid. (See back cover).

Could be confused with
Polytrichum species: *Dicranum* leaves are softer and glossier. They stay in same positions whether moist or dry.

Dicranum majus: see opposite. *D. scoparium* tolerates a wider range of conditions and is more widespread and common.

Leucobryum glaucum which is white-green, forms denser cushions, and its leaves are often spongy and waterlogged.

Dicranum majus Great Fork Moss

Habitats

Mountain ledges and upland woods in Ireland and north and west Britain.

Main NVC woodland types:
W11, W17, W18d/e, W19.

Key ID features

Up to 15 cm tall in loose tufts.

Leaves glossy yellow to dark green, 9 - 15 mm long. They are strongly falcate and all curve to one side. The long fine leaf tips are toothed all round.

Up to 6 capsules, each on straw-yellow seta can arise from a single head. Capsules are dark green-brown and lightly furrowed. (See back cover).

Microhabitats

Rotting wood, tree bases, humus banks, among rocks, cliff ledges.

Acidic ground. Needs shade so usually a woodland plant.

Could be confused with:

Dicranum scoparium.

D. majus is taller and looser in habit than *D. scoparium.* Its leaves are longer and more uniformly falcate. The leaf tip teeth are shorter, sharper and more numerous than in *D. scoparium.*

D. scoparium setae are always solitary unlike in *D. majus.* The latter's capsules are shorter and broader.

Atrichum undulatum   Catherine's Moss

Habitats

Heath, open wasteland, many types of woodland especially:

Main NVC woodland types:

W7, W8, W9, W10, W11.

Microhabitats

Banks, clearings, by burns.

Often on bare acid to basic soil, not extremes: loam, clay, humus.

Key ID features

Upright, unbranched stems 2 - 7 cm tall.

Widely spreading lingulate to lanceolate leaves with toothed margins. These are strongly undulate when moist, shrivelled and curled when dry. They are longer near top of stem: 6 - 9 mm. Leaves are soft, translucent and deep or yellow-green.

Seta red, 2-4 cm. Capsule cylindrical, narrow and curved to one side, with long beak.

Could be confused with:

Plagiomnium undulatum which has undulate leaves with blunt tips; *A. undulatum* leaves taper to acute tips. *P. undulatum* often has branched stems.

Mnium hornum which has unbranched stems but its leaves are not undulate. It fruits in late spring; *A. undulatum* fruits in autumn/winter.

Plagiomnium undulatum   Palm Moss

Habitats

Widespread in woodlands. Also on dune slacks and marshy ground.

Main NVC woodland types:
W5, W7, W8, W9.

Microhabitats

Grass banks, rock clefts, soil or soil-covered rocks.

Prefers fertile neutral soils. Needs shade and moisture.

Key ID features

Well-grown stems branched near tips giving dendroid appearance; many stems unbranched and arched. Fertile stems have rosette of branches at top.

Leaves pale green, spreading and filmy. They are strongly undulate when moist; curled and twisted when dry. Leaves are lingulate with nerve protruding from blunt tip. Longest leaves are 8-12 mm

Male plants can have open flower-like tips but are rarely fertile. 2 - 10 capsules can arise from a rosette, on orange seta 3 cm long. Capsules are brown, pear-shaped and pendulous.

Could be confused with:

Atrichum undulatum and *Mnium hornum* both of which have a double line of teeth along leaf margins; *P undulatum* has only a single line of teeth. *P undulatum* has blunt leaf tips, the other two species have finely pointed leaf tips

Mnium hornum   Forest Star

Habitats

Woodland plant at low altitudes. Mountain ledges.

Main NVC woodland types: W3, W4, W5, W7, W10, W11, W15, W16, W17, W18.

Key ID features

In dull yellow to dark green tufts or carpets. Red-brown stems rarely exceed 5 cm. In spring, light green tips contrast with older growth.

Crowded, spreading, oval, toothed leaves to 4 mm, narrowing to acute tips. They curl when dry; are not wavy when moist.

Seta 2.5 - 5 cm with one fine pendulous capsule per plant. Fruiting common.

Microhabitats

Banks and hollows, rotting logs and stumps, tree bases, on/among rocks, burnsides.

Acid, well-drained soils and humus. Sometimes on peat. Shaded positions.

Could be confused with:

Atrichum undulatum which is larger with longer, undulate, more translucent, leaves. Its capsule is curved and long, not pendulous and blunt as in *M. hornum.*

Plagiomnium undulatum which has some branched stems and all leaves undulate; *M. hornum* has neither. *P. undulatum* rarely fruits and would have several capsules per plant unlike *M. hornum.*

Rhizomnium punctatum   Round Moss

Habitats

Fens, marshes, mountains, swamp or wet woods.

Microhabitats

Typically wet stony ground by burns. Tree stumps, rock clefts, base of wet rock faces.

Main NVC woodland types: W3, W5, W7.

Mildly acid to basic soil/ humus or rock in wet shaded conditions.

Key ID features

Robust, erect, red-brown stems 1 - 10 cm tall as tufts, patches or scattered plants.

Leaves small, oval and widely spaced at base of stem, increasing in size upwards, often forming a wide funnel at shoot tip.

Key ID continued

Leaves light to deep green, translucent with tiny dots and a thick border. They are obovate 6 - 8 mm long, 4 - 5 mm across with a wide blunt apex. Apex often has a short apiculus.

Capsule narrowly ovoid with long beak on lid.

Could be confused with:

Mnium hornum has softer, less glossy, narrow, pointed leaves, which are wider at base. It is not found in wet microhabitats.

Thuidium tamariscinum   Tamarisk Moss

Habitats

Hedges, grassland, broadleaved and conifer woodlands, particularly in W.

Main NVC woodland types: W4, W9, W11, W17, W19.

Microhabitats

Soil, rocky or grassy banks; tree stems and branches; tree stumps and rotting wood; rocks.

On acid to basic substrates, including heavy clay. Often in shady places.

Key ID features

Green stem, often blackish at base, 10-20 cm long. Forms mats with stems and branches interwoven.

Fine, fern-like branching. Fronds are tripinnate and bright green in shade; vivid yellow-green where more open.

Stem leaves triangular to heart-shaped, branch leaves narrower and minute, both with finely acute, toothed apices. Base of stem often sparsely leafy, apex of stem often without branches.

Fruiting rare except in wetter north and west. It often produces new plants vegetatively, rooting along stem.

Could be confused with:

Hylocomium splendens which also has fern-like branching. However the *H. splendens* stem is bright red rather than green, the branching is at most bip-innate and the leaves are golden rather than vivid green.

Eurhynchium praelongum also has green stems but they are not robust. Branching is less elaborate - at most bipinnate

Hylocomium splendens Step Moss

Habitats
Heaths, moorland, grassland, fixed dunes, mountains and upland woods.

Main NVC woodland types:
W4, W11, W17, W18, W19.

Key ID features
Bright red or red-brown stem with silky, glossy, yellow-green to yellow-brown shoots. Forms loose carpets.

New shoots grow up and along from old, giving a stepped look. Fronds bipinnately branched.

Stem leaves to 3 mm and broadly ovate, narrowing abruptly into straight, toothed tips. Branch leaves smaller with shorter point. Leaves concave with double nerve.

Short, broad, curved capsules occasional, on 2 - 5 cm seta.

Microhabitats
Turf or rocky banks, mountain ledges. With grass, heather and other mosses.

Well-drained acid to neutral, or leached basic soil.

Could be confused with:

Pleurozium schreberi which is singly-pinnate and has larger branch leaves. (Also in picture above).

Thuidium tamariscinum which is tripinnate, has a green stem (blackish lower down) and no gloss.

Isothecium myosuroides Mouse-tail

Habitats
Woods and mountain ledges especially in west.

Main NVC woodland types:
W11, W17.

Microhabitats
Tree branches, bases, stems; rotting stumps and logs; rocks and walls.

Acid to neutral substrate. In damp and shade - more in open in west.

Key ID features

Forms pale yellow or mid-green mats. Curved or upright shoots 1- 2 cm long and sub-dendroid near finely pointed tips; branching sparser near base of shoots. Branches often point in same direction.

Branch leaves narrowly ovate to lanceolate, drawn into fine points. Stem leaves larger and sometimes broader. All leaves straight with finely toothed edges.

Orange-red seta 1-2 cm long with slightly curved, ovoid capsule of 2-2.5 mm. It is shortly pointed and held at an angle.

Could be confused with:

Isothecium alopecuroides which is scarcer in acid habitats. It has blunt, concave leaves with apiculate tips. Its capsule is held erect.

Isothecium alopecuroides Big Mouse-tail

Habitats

Low-altitude woodland and rock habitats.

Main NVC woodland types:
W8, W9, W11, W17.

Key ID features

Forms extensive yellow to grey-green mats. Secondary stems sub-dendroid: unbranched for 1 - 3 cm, freely branched above. Upper branches crowded and often curved to one side.

Branches appear swollen with concave, overlapping leaves. Leaf is ovate-oblong with blunt tip often with short apiculus.

Occasional red-brown, symmetrical, erect capsules, with long-beaked lids, in autumn and winter.

Microhabitats

Tree bases and stems; rotting stumps and logs; rocks and screes; by burns.

Dry to moist, neutral to basic substrate. Likes shade.

Could be confused with:

Isothecium myosuroides which also has sub-dendroid branches. It is less robust than *I. alopecuroides* and its leaves have long fine tips.

I. alopecuroides has larger leaves and their margins are less strongly toothed than those of *I. myosuroides*.

Eurhynchium striatum   Stripe Moss

Habitats

Hedges, woodlands, grassy sea cliffs.

Microhabitats

Banks, grass, damp turf, soil, rocks, logs. By burns.

Main NVC woodland types:
W8, W9.

Neutral to basic fertile rock and soil, including clay. Likes shade.

Key ID features

Robust, medium-sized moss growing in loose, glossy, yellow to dark green masses. Arched secondary stems are freely branched and wiry giving a bushy appearance. Stems green and stout.

Leaves are strongly plicate when dry giving a striped look. Stem leaf 1.5 - 2 mm long, triangular to heart-shaped with decurrent base and pronounced auricles. Branch leaves similar but smaller. Both types of leaf taper to short acute apex and have strongly toothed margins.

Fruiting occasional in autumn/winter. Smooth seta 2 - 3.5 cm long with curved, cylindrical, red-brown, long-beaked capsules.

Could be confused with:

Hylocomium brevirostre also has a wiry, bushy appearance, but has a red stem, and is mostly western.

Brachythecium rutabulum is another robust, green-stemmed moss. It lacks the rigid bushy aspect and plicate leaves of *E. striatum*. *B. rutabulum* leaves are drawn into longer points than those of *E. striatum*.

Eurhynchium praelongum Feather Moss

Habitats
Fields, marshes, hedgerows and woodlands, usually in the lowlands.

Microhabitats
Earthy banks, grassy places, tree bases, tree stumps, burn and ditch sides.

Main NVC woodland types:
W1, W5, W6, W7, W8, W9, W10, W11.

Neutral to basic fertile soils, including clays. Likes damp. Very shade tolerant - often the only moss in dark places

Key ID features

Delicate pale yellow to mid-green moss forming loose to dense mats. Main stem to 12 cm, with regularly pinnate, and sometimes bipinnate, frond-like, slender branches.

Stem leaves triangular. Branch leaves smaller and narrower. All leaves finely pointed.

Capsules common, curved with long-beaked lids, held on rough seta 2 - 3 cm long.

Could be confused with:

Thuidium tamariscinum is stiffer, often tripinnate and has shorter branch leaves. It is brighter green.

Eurhynchium striatum has thicker, stiffer, irregular branches with broader plicate leaves.

Difference in size and shape between stem leaves and branch leaves more marked in *Eurynchium praelongum* than in most moss species.

Calliergonella cuspidata   Spear Moss

Habitats

Moist pastures, marshland, calcareous bogs, dune slacks. Damp woods.

Main NVC woodland types: W3, W5, W7.

Microhabitats

Mud, flushes, by burns and pools, moist turf, woodland rides.

On wet ground with neutral to basic soils.

Key ID features

Upright shoots, from creeping primary stem, in tufts, patches or scattered. Shoots have spear-head tip formed of young, tightly rolled leaves. Plant is yellow-green to orange-brown in colour, with a glossy texture.

Stems reddish, to 12 cm, with widely-spaced, pinnate branching. Large, broad, ovate leaves on shoots, to 2.5 mm. Narrower leaves on branches. Both leaf types have a wide base, taper to a blunt rounded apex and have untoothed margins.

Fruiting is uncommon. The large curved capsule is carried on a long, 5 - 7 cm, red seta.

Could be confused with:

Pleurozium schreberi which also has red stems but grows in drier acid habitats. It has less pointed shoot and branch tips, is often a lighter green (orange and brown leaves absent) and lacks the golden gloss of *C. cuspidata*.

Brachythecium rutabulum Ordinary Moss

Habitats
Marshes, grassland, heaths, lawns, fields, cliffs, hedgerows, woodlands.

Main NVC woodland types:
W5, W6, W7, W8.

Microhabitats
Tree bases and branches, stumps and logs, rocks, walls, soil, turf, banks by burns and rivers, roadsides.

Neutral to basic substrate, damp shaded conditions.

Key ID features

Variable moss with lack of distinctive features (i.e. ordinary). Glossy pale or yellow-green to bright green and robust. Green stems to 12 cm with short, irregularly branched shoots, forming loose mats or as scattered stems below field layer.

Leaves spreading, large (2-3 mm), broadly ovate, slightly plicate when moist and tapering to acute tips. Leaf margins have minute teeth.

Unbeaked capsule 2.5 - 3.5 mm, on rough seta 1.5 - 3 cm long. Common.

Could be confused with:

Brachythecium rivulare has pale spear-like branch tips. Its leaves are less spreading with shorter tips. It is golden green and found in moister waterside habitats.

Cirriphyllum piliferum has leaves which taper to long, very fine hair points.

Scleropodium purum Neat Moss

Habitats
Upland and coastal heaths, sand-dunes, grassland, open conifer and broadleaved woodlands.

Microhabitats
Grassy banks, short turf, woodland rides and clearings.

Main NVC woodland types:
W11, W17, W18, W19.

Acid to basic soils. Not tolerant of deep shade.

Key ID features

Robust, light green, sometimes almost translucent moss which forms lax patches.

Pale green stems to 15 cm, with regularly pinnate branching and blunt shoot tips. Densely overlapping leaves give stems a stout swollen appearance.

Leaf large, to 2 mm wide, concave, blunt, with a tiny, pointed, recurved apiculus and lightly toothed margins.

Fruiting rare.

Could be confused with:
Pleurozium schreberi has a red stem, more pointed shoot tips and blunter-tipped leaves.

Brachythecium rutabulum has spreading, finely-pointed leaves and its branching is more irregular.

Pleurozium schreberi   Red-stem

Habitats
Lowland and upland heaths, grasslands, mountain slopes, conifer and broadleaved woods.

Main NVC woodland types:
W11, W17, W18, W19.

Key ID features

Robust, glossy, yellow to light green moss with bright red stem, which grows in thick mats.

Stems to 12 cm, often slightly curved, with pinnate branching. Ends of branches often drawn into fine points.

Leaves broadly ovate, slightly inrolled at edges with blunt tips. Stem leaves larger than branch leaves.

Fruiting rare.

Microhabitats

Banks, peaty ledges, often with grasses and mosses such as *Hylocomium splendens*.

Acid to strongly acid soils and humus. Good indicator of acid substrate.

Could be confused with:
Scleropodium purum has a stouter green stem, blunter shoot tips and its leaves are apiculate.

Hylocomium splendens (also in main picture) usually has bipinnate branching and has smaller branch leaves.

Calliergonella cuspidata grows in wetter, more neutral to basic habitats. It has straighter stems and branches with pronounced spear-like tips. Leaves have decurrent auricles.

27

Plagiothecium undulatum Wavy flat-moss

Habitats
Upland bog and heath, mountains, woodlands especially in north and west.

Microhabitats
Banks on soil or with grasses and bryophytes; logs, rocks, under heather, ditch and burn-banks.

Main NVC woodland types: W11, W17, W18, W19.

Acidic substrate including humus and leached soils. Seeks moisture and shade.

Key ID features

Robust, flattened, soft, shiny, pale to whitish-green moss forming patches or loose mats.

Stems to 12 cm and little-branched.

Large undulate leaves 2.5 - 4 mm long, overlap in two opposite rows. Leaves ovate with short acute apex.

Fruiting occasional. Long, curved capsule on orange-red seta 2 - 4 cm long.

Could be confused with:

Plagiothecium denticulatum, P. nemorale and *P. succulentum* also have flattened shoots but their leaves are darker green and not undulate.

Ptilium crista-castrensis   Plume Moss

Habitats

Mainly in pine, oak and birch woodland, but also in some heaths.

Main NVC woodland types: W17, W18

Microhabitats

With dwarf shrubs, litter and other mosses on forest floor. In soil among boulders.

Moist acid substrate including humus.

Key ID features

Erect feathery, medium-sized, bright or golden-green moss. Grows in loose patches or dense tufts.

Single stems generally 5 - 8 cm long with crowded, regularly pinnate branching.

Leaves taper to long points which curl in a circle, all leaves curled in same direction.

Fruiting rare.

Hypnum cupressiforme complex

Creeping to erect mat-forming mosses with irregular to pinnate branching and straight to strongly falcate, finely pointed leaves. Leaves often overlap as on cypress branches. Found in most habitats, often growing on rocks or bark.

Hypnum andoi

Hypnum cupressiforme (Ben Averis)

Hypnum cupressiforme

Hypnum jutlandicum (both below)

Ben Averis

Hypnum lacunosum (three above)

Cypress Mosses

Species	Habitats	Key ID features	Microhabitats
Wood NVC types			
Hypnum andoi	Mainly in sheltered woodland, especially in north and west.	Very slender to medium-sized moss, forming yellow to golden-green mats. Irregularly branched. Leaves falcate to strongly falcate. Capsule with conical lid.	Tree trunks and rocks.
W11, W17.			Acid substrate, humid sheltered conditions.
Hypnum cupressiforme	Woods, grasslands, rock habitats.	Very slender to medium-sized moss growing in patches or carpets. Light to dark green, often glossy when dry. Irregular branching. Weakly falcate to falcate leaves. Capsule curved or inclined and rostrate.	Tree stems and branches, logs, rock, walls.
Trees/rocks in W9, W10, W11, W15, W16, W17, W18, W19.	On trees in W1, W3, W4, W7.		Acid substrate. Can withstand exposed conditions.
Hypnum jutlandicum	Heaths, bogs, grasslands, mountains, broadleaved and conifer woodlands.	Medium-sized to robust. Forms lax, pale or silvery-green mats. Regularly pinnate branching, shoots flattened. Leaves slightly overlapping and falcate. Capsules rare - curved or horizontal with rostrate lid.	On forest floor or steep banks, often with dwarf shrubs.
W17, W18, W19.			Mainly on acidic soil, humus or litter.
Hypnum lacunosum	Grassland, sand-dunes, open woodlands.	Robust yellow-green to golden-brown, glossy moss. Irregularly branched, branches swollen with crowded very concave leaves. Leaves strongly falcate. Capsule curved/inclined, lid rostrate.	Rocks, walls, soil, sand, turf.
W8, W9.			Mainly on well-lit, basic substrate.
Hypnum resupinatum	Most common in woodlands.	Very slender to slender, pale green to dark-olive green silky mat-forming moss. Branching irregular. Leaves almost straight or slightly bent, lacking cypress branch character. Capsule erect or slightly curved with long beak.	Bark, logs, rocks and walls.
W7, W9, W11, W17.			Acid to slightly basic substrate. Prefers light shade.

Rhytidiadelphus squarrosus Lawn Moss

Habitats
Moist grassland, lawns, sand-dunes, marshes, heaths, mountains, woods.

Main NVC woodland types:
W11, W17, W19.

Microhabitats
Banks, roadsides, rides, often with grass or on humus.

Acid to neutral substrate, can tolerate basic soils. Prefers damp conditions.

Key ID features

Straggly moss which forms dense patches or loose mats. Pale green to yellow with bright red stems. Slender, weak stems 5 - 13 cm long, irregularly pinnately or sparsely branched.

Stem leaves 2 - 3 mm long, triangular, squarrose and arranged round stem, forming a star at stem tip. Branch leaves smaller and narrower.

Fruiting rare.

Could be confused with:

Rhytidiadelphus loreus has longer stiffer stems, without 'starry' tips and grows in larger mats. It has falcate leaves, all curved to one side, which are plicate.

Rhytidiadelphus loreus   Stiff Moss

Habitats
Heaths, bogs, rocky areas, grasslands, snow-beds, upland woods particularly in N and W.

Microhabitats
Woodland floor on soil or rocks, fallen logs.

Main NVC woodland types:
W11, W17, W18, W19.

Acid soil, humid conditions.

Key ID features

Robust yellow to olive-green moss growing in coarse patches or large masses. Stiff, red to orange-brown stem, to 15 cm long, is pinnately or sparingly branched.

Large (to 3 mm), crowded, strongly plicate, falcate leaves. Leaves triangular tapering to long toothed tip, all curving same way along branch.

Could be confused with:

Rhytidiadelphus squarrosus is shorter and weaker. Its leaves are squarrose and not strongly plicate.

Short curved capsules, with pointed lids, occasional. Red seta 3 cm long.

Rhytidiadelphus triquetrus Shaggy Moss

Habitats
Sand-dunes, grassland, heath, moor, mountain ledges, roadsides, woods especially in N & E.

Microhabitats
Banks, woodland clearings and edges, on soil or with grass/dwarf shrubs.

Main NVC woodland types:
W9, W11, W17d, W18a/b/c, W19.

Mainly neutral to basic soil, including clay, but also common on acid soils in N & E.

Key ID features

Large, robust moss growing in loose mats or coarse tufts. Stout, red, rigid, erect stem to 20 cm with short branches of different lengths all round, giving bushy appearance.

Pale yellow to bright green leaves, widely spreading. Leaves triangular, pointed, straight and plicate, with toothed margins. Stem leaves 3 - 6 mm long.

Fruiting rare.

Could be confused with:

Rhytidiadelphus loreus. It has curved, finely pointed leaves.

Diplophyllum albicans Doublewort

Habitats

Mountain ledges, lowland banks, woodlands.

Main NVC woodland types:
W11, W17.

Microhabitats
On or under heathy banks and rocky ledges; rock faces, boulders, soil.

Acid soils, including peat and sand. Likes moisture.

Key ID features

Leafy liverwort forming white to dark green, often orange or brown-tinted, tufts or wide patches.

Stems 1- 5 cm, sometimes branched, with two regular ranks of leaves.

Each leaf divided near base into two lobes, the smaller bent back to lie on larger so appearing like four rows of leaves. Each leaf roughly oblong with blunt, irregularly toothed tip.

Light band down middle of each leaf. It is the only liverwort to have such a feature.

Lophocolea bidentata Pincerwort

Habitats

Moist lawns and grassland, woodland.

Main NVC woodland types:

W4, W5, W7, W9, W11, W17, W18, W19.

Key ID features

Flat, pale white-green, translucent, leafy liverwort. Stems 1 - 4 cm long, slender and sparsely branched. In pure patches or lax interweavings.

Leaves in two regular ranks, well spaced or slightly overlapping. Leaves have two finely-pointed lobes.

Fruiting common.

Microhabitats

Soil on woodland floor, banks, among rocks, grasses and mosses. Also on rotting timber.

Could be confused with:

Lophocolea heterophylla which has many leaves unlobed (especially at shoot tips). It is markedly lowland.

Lophozia ventricosa which has firmer more opaque leaves which stick out from the stem in such a way that the shoot is not as flat as in *Lophocolea bidentata*.

Pellia epiphylla   Dripwort

Habitats
Mountains, rock habitats and woods.

Main NVC woodland types:
W5, W7, W9, W17a.

Key ID features

Thalloid liverwort with flattened, irregularly branched and wavy-edged thalli to 1 cm wide, often massed together to form large patches.

Dull green; darker near central midrib; paler and more translucent towards edges. Thallus surface smooth and often moist.

Microhabitats
Banks, rock faces, below rock ledges, burn and ditch sides.

Moist to wet, acid to neutral rock and soil, including clay, loam and peat. In shade.

Could be confused with:

Pellia neesiana is less common and grows in wet habitats, has its capsule arising from an erect, tubular rather than a horizontal, flattened sheath or "involucre".

Pellia endiviifolia has a narrower thallus (to 5 mm), which is often much forked at tip, and is found on wet calcareous substrate.

Conocephalum conicum has a thicker, larger (to 1.5 cm wide) shinier, brighter green thallus with numerous pale dots. It is found on neutral to basic substrate.

Commonest bryophytes in Scottish

NVC Code	Community or sub-community name	Commonest bryophytes
	WET WILLOW-ALDER-BIRCH WOODLAND	
W1	*Salix cinerea-Galium palustre* Grey willow-marsh bedstraw woodland	*Eurhynchium praelongum.*
W3	*Salix pentandra-Carex rostrata* Bay willow-bottle sedge woodland	*Calliergonella cuspidata, Mnium hornum, Rhizomnium punctatum.*
W4	*Betula pubescens-Molinia caerulea*	Downy birch-purple moor grass wood
W4a	*Dryopteris dilatata-Rubus fruticosus* Male fern-bramble sub-community	*Mnium hornum, Hylocomium splendens, Thuidium tamariscinum.*
W4b W4c	*Juncus effusus:* soft rush sub-community *Sphagnum* sub-community	As W4a **plus** *Polytrichum commune, Sphagnum fallax, Sphagnum palustre.*
W5	*Alnus glutinosa-Carex paniculata* Common alder–greater tussock sedge woodland	*Eurhynchium praelongum, Mnium hornum, Rhizomnium punctatum, Plagiomnium undulatum, Pellia epiphylla, Calliergonella cuspidata, Brachythecium rutabulum,*
W6	*Alnus glutinosa-Urtica dioica* Common alder-nettle woodland	*Brachythecium rutabulum, Eurhynchium praelongum.*
W7	*Alnus glutinosa-Fraxinus excelsior-Lysimachia nemorum:* Common alder-yellow pimpernel woodland	*Brachythecium rutabulum, Lophocolea bidentata, Eurhynchium praelongum, Calliergonella cuspidata, Rhizomnium punctatum, Pellia epiphylla, Mnium hornum, Plagiomnium undulatum.*
	HERB-RICH ASH-ELM-SYCAMORE-HAZEL WOODLAND	
W8	*Fraxinus excelsior-Acer campestre-Mercurialis perennis* Ash-field maple-dog's mercury woodland	*Eurhynchium striatum, Eurhynchium praelongum, Plagiomnium undulatum Brachythecium rutabulum.*
W9	*Fraxinus excelsior-Sorbus aucuparia-Mercurialis perennis* Ash-rowan-dog's mercury woodland	*Eurhynchium praelongum, E. striatum, Thuidium tamariscinum, Lophocolea bidentata, Plagiomnium undulatum.*
	OAK-BIRCH-ROWAN-HAZEL WOODLAND WITH GRASS OR BRACKEN	
W10	*Quercus robur-Rubus fruticosus-Pteridium aquilinum-woodland* Pedunculate oak-bramble-bracken wood	*Eurhynchium praelongum, Mnium hornum.*
W11	*Quercus petraea-Betula pubescens-Oxalis acetosella* Sessile oak-downy birch-wood sorrel woodland	*Eurhynchium praelongum, Dicranum scoparium, Hylocomium splendens, Polytrichum formosum, Thuidium tamariscinum, Pleurozium schreberi, Mnium hornum, Scleropodium purum, Rhytidiadelphus squarrosus, Rhytidiadelphus triquetrus.*

NVC woodland communities

W16	*Quercus* **spp.-** *Betula* **spp.-** *Deschampsia flexuosa* Oak-birch-wavy-hair grass woodland	*Dicranum scoparium, Mnium hornum, Polytrichum formosum, Hypnum cupressiforme/jutlandicum.*
	BEECHWOOD	
W15	*Fagus sylvatica-Deschampsia flexuosa* Beech-wavy-hair grass woodland	*Hypnum cupressiforme, Leucobryum glaucum, Mnium hornum, Polytrichum formosum.*
	OAK-BIRCH-ROWAN WOODLAND WITH HEATH OR MOSS-RICH	
W17	*Quercus petraea-Betula pubescens-Dicranum majus*	Sessile oak-downy birch-*Dicranum majus* woodland
W17a	*Isothecium myosuroides-Diplophyllum albicans* sub-community	As W17b/c **plus** *Diplophyllum albicans, Isothecium myosuroides, Leucobryum glaucum, Lophocolea bidentata.*
W17b	Typical sub-community	*Dicranum majus, Dicranum scoparium, Hylocomium splendens, Pleurozium schreberi, Mnium hornum, Hypnum jutlandicum, Rhytidiadelphus loreus, Polytrichum formosum, Thuidium tamariscinum, Plagiothecium undulatum.*
W17c	*Anthoxanthum odoratum-Agrostis capillaris* Sweet vernal grass-common bent sub-community	
W17d	*Rhytidiadelphus triquetrus* sub-community	As W17b/c **minus** *Mnium hornum,* **plus** *Rhytidiadelphus triquetrus.*
	NATIVE CONIFER WOODLAND	
W18	*Pinus sylvestris-Hylocomium splendens*	Scot's pine-*Hylocomium splendens* woodland
W18a	*Goodyera repens-Erica cinerea:* creeping lady's tresses-bell heather sub-community	*Dicranum scoparium, Hylocomium splendens, Hypnum jutlandicum, Mnium hornum, Rhytidiadelphus triquetrus, Rhytidiadelphus loreus, Pleurozium schreberi, Scleropodium purum, Plagiothecium undulatum, Ptilium crista-castrensis.*
W18b	*Vaccinium myrtillus-Vaccinium vitis-idaea* Blaeberry-cowberry sub-community	
W18c	*Luzula pilosa* Hairy woodrush sub-community	
W18d	*Sphagnum capillifolium/quinquefarium-Erica tetralix: Sphagnum*-cross-leaved heath sub-community	As W18a/b/c **plus** *Dicranum majus* and *Sphagnum capillifolium/ quinquefarium* **minus** *Rhytidiadelphus triquetrus.*
W18e	*Scapania gracilis* sub-community	
W19	*Juniperus communis-Oxalis acetosella* Juniper-wood sorrel woodland	*Hylocomium splendens, Thuidium tamariscinum, Dicranum scoparium, Dicranum majus, Plagiothecium undulatum, Rhytidiadelphus loreus, Pleurozium schreberi, Hypnum jutlandicum, Rhytidiadelphus triquetrus, Scleropodium purum.*

References and sources of information

References

Blockeel T.L. and Long D.G. (1998): **A Check-list and Census Catalogue of British and Irish Bryophytes**. British Bryological Society. Cardiff.

The distribution of bryophytes (by vice-counties). Also most up to date list of species names (which do change).

Paton J.A. (1999): **The Liverwort Flora of the British Isles.** Harley Books, Colchester, Essex.

The definitive guide to liverworts with excellent drawings of microscopic features.

Perry A.R. (1992): **Mosses and Liverworts of Woodland.** A Guide to Some of the Commonest Species. British Plant Life Number 1. National Museum of Wales.

An introductory guide to common British species. Black & white illustrations and text for 29 species; colour photos of a further 10 species.

Rodwell J.S. (Ed) (1991): **British Plant Communities Volume 1 - Woodlands and Scrub**. Cambridge University Press.

Detailed information on the NVC communities mentioned in this booklet.

Smith A.J. E (1978): **The Moss Flora of Britain & Ireland.**
Smith A.J. E (1990): **The Liverwort Flora of Britain & Ireland.** Both Cambridge University Press.

The standard floras and guides to microscopic features. 700 mosses and 300 liverworts included. Black & white line drawings.

Watson E.V. (1981): **British Mosses and Liverworts**. Third Edition. Cambridge University Press.

Best field guide. 200 commonest species in depth plus notes on additional species. Black & white illustrations.

Watson H. (1947): **Woodland Mosses**. Forestry Commission Booklet No. 1. HMSO. London.

20 mosses covered. Black and white photographs of group and shoot. Long out of print. Slightly confusing because of moss name changes. Historical interest.

Sources of further information

Kindrogan Field Centre in Scotland (Tel: 01250 881286) and the Field Study Council, England & Wales (www.field-studies-council.org) run bryophyte courses.

The Native Woodlands Discussion Group runs occasional workshops on woodland bryophyte ID. See www.nwdg.org.uk for how to join NWDG.

A Lower Plants Section of NWDG has been formed to bring together people who wish to study mosses, liverworts, lichens and fungi. Details from Ben Averis. Tel: 01620 860029, email: abg.am.averis@virgin.net